JF CUT Graphic
Cyber Patrol

Cutting, Robert

15584
Epsom Public Library

Y0-BQS-345

DISCARD

DISCARD

DISCARD

Literacy Consultants
DAVID BOOTH • KATHLEEN GOULD LUNDY

Social Studies Consultant
PETER PAPPAS

A Harcourt Achieve Imprint

10801 N. Mopac Expressway
Building # 3
Austin, TX 78759
1.800.531.5015

Steck-Vaughn is a trademark of Harcourt Achieve Inc. registered in the United
States of America and/or other jurisdictions. All inquiries should be mailed to:
Paralegal Department, 6277 Sea Harbor Drive, Orlando, FL 32887.

Ru'bĭcon © 2007 Rubicon Publishing Inc.
www. rubiconpublishing.com

All rights reserved. No part of this publication may be reproduced or transmitted in
any form or by any means, electronic or mechanical, including photocopying, recording,
taping, or any information storage and retrieval system, without permission in writing
from the copyright owner.

Project Editor: Kim Koh
Editor: Vicki Low
Editorial Assistants: Caitlin Drake, Joyce Thian
Art Director: Jen Harvey
Project Designer: Jan-John Rivera

7 8 9 10 11   5 4 3 2 1

Cyber Patrol
ISBN 13: 978-1-4190-3223-3
ISBN 10:   1-4190-3223-2

Printed in Singapore

CYBER PATROL

Written by
ROBERT CUTTING

Illustrated by
JIM GRAVES

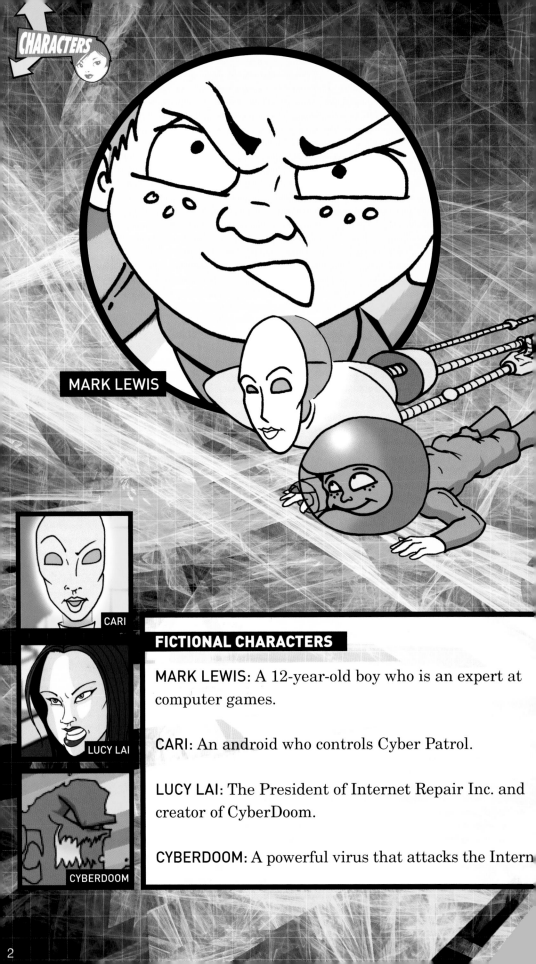

MARK LEWIS

CARI

LUCY LAI

CYBERDOOM

FICTIONAL CHARACTERS

MARK LEWIS: A 12-year-old boy who is an expert at computer games.

CARI: An android who controls Cyber Patrol.

LUCY LAI: The President of Internet Repair Inc. and creator of CyberDoom.

CYBERDOOM: A powerful virus that attacks the Intern

Contents

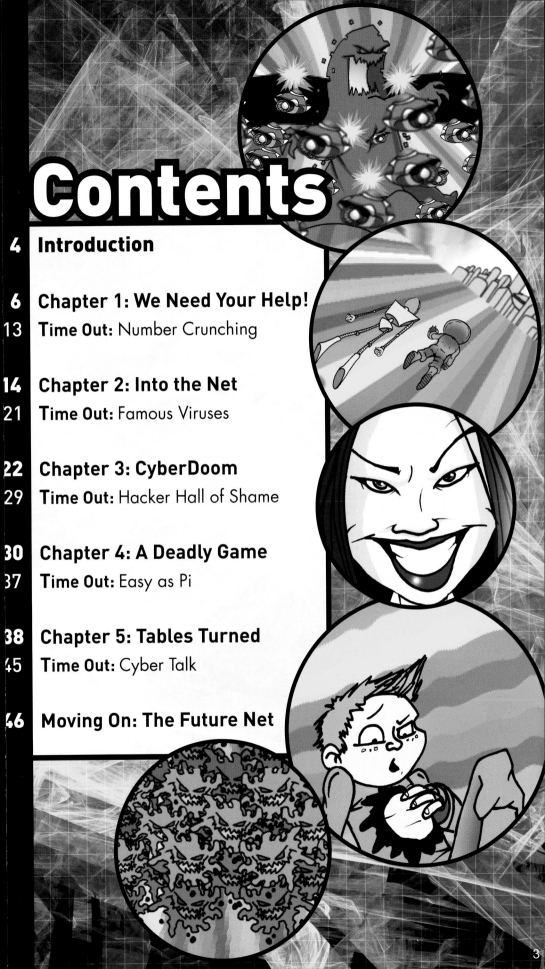

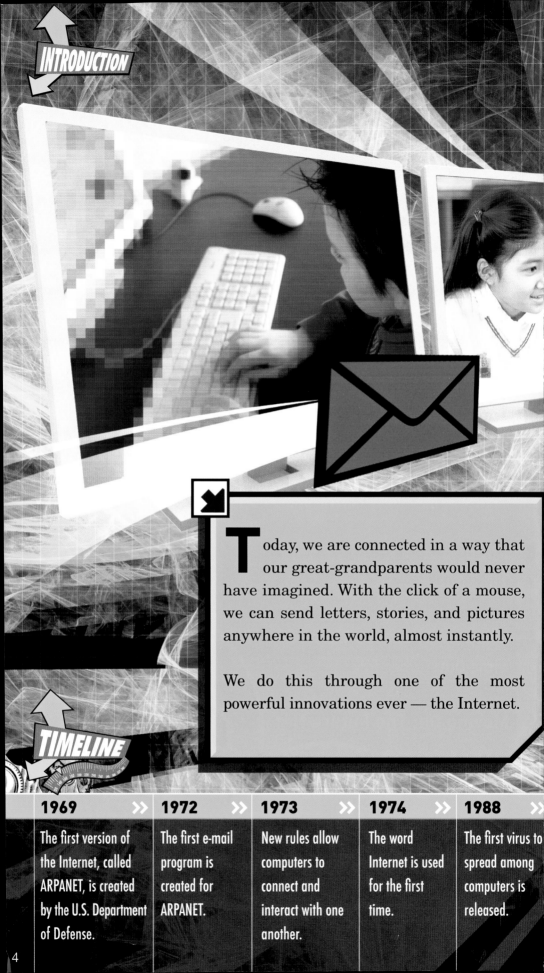

Today, we are connected in a way that our great-grandparents would never have imagined. With the click of a mouse, we can send letters, stories, and pictures anywhere in the world, almost instantly.

We do this through one of the most powerful innovations ever — the Internet.

TIMELINE

1969 >>	1972 >>	1973 >>	1974 >>	1988 >>
The first version of the Internet, called ARPANET, is created by the U.S. Department of Defense.	The first e-mail program is created for ARPANET.	New rules allow computers to connect and interact with one another.	The word Internet is used for the first time.	The first virus to spread among computers is released.

For computer users who play online games, the Internet is more than a place for getting information. It is cyberspace, a virtual world where they can have adventures in 3D.

In the future, a trip into cyberspace could be a reality. But what awaits us there?

WHAT'S THE STORY? This story is set in an imaginary future. Its characters and events are fictitious.

1983	1990	1993	1996	2006
The Domain Name System is created. Website addresses can now be written as names, not	Tim Berners-Lee creates the World Wide Web.	The first web browser is created, allowing Internet users to search, retrieve, and display data and	New ideas are introduced for the next generation of the Internet – Internet 2.	There are mo than 20 billio web pages, a counting ...

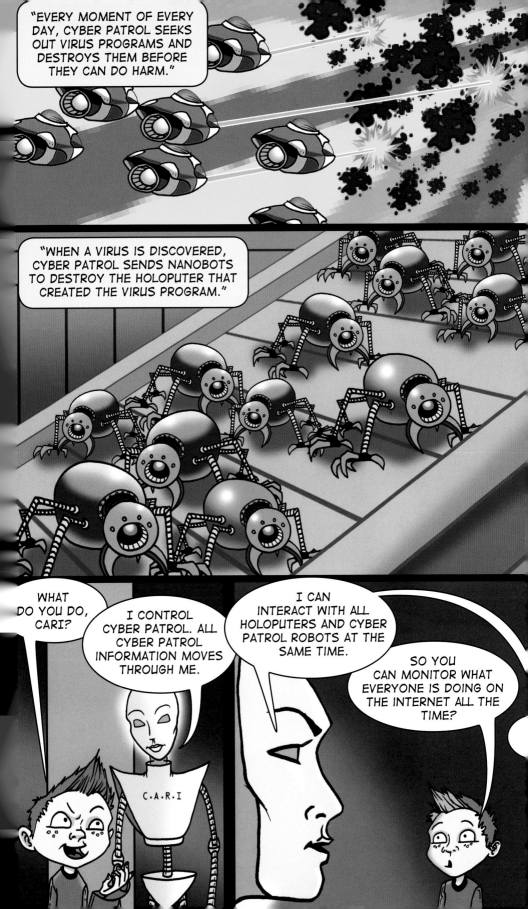

NUMBER CRUNCHING

1 billion — Estimated number of people in the world using the Internet in 2006. The world population at the time was 6.5 billion.

70 million — Number of American households with one or more computers as of 2003.

80,000 — Average number of blogs created each day since 2003. Blog is the short form of "web log" and refers to an online journal.

2,000 — Number of new lawsuits worldwide against illegal music file sharers.

325 — Number of legal online music sites in the world as of April 2006.

31 — Average number of hours Internet users spent online per month as of March 2006.

I'M HUMAN — I *CAN'T* BE IN THE INTERNET!
THE HELMET AND ARMOR YOU PUT ON TURNED YOU INTO A PROGRAM.
C.A.R.I
I'VE BECOME A PROGRAM?
YES, MARK LEWIS.
THIS IS A MAP OF THE INTERNET. CYBERDOOM WAS LAST HERE, IN THE EURASIAN NET.
C.A.R.I
HOW DO WE GET THERE?

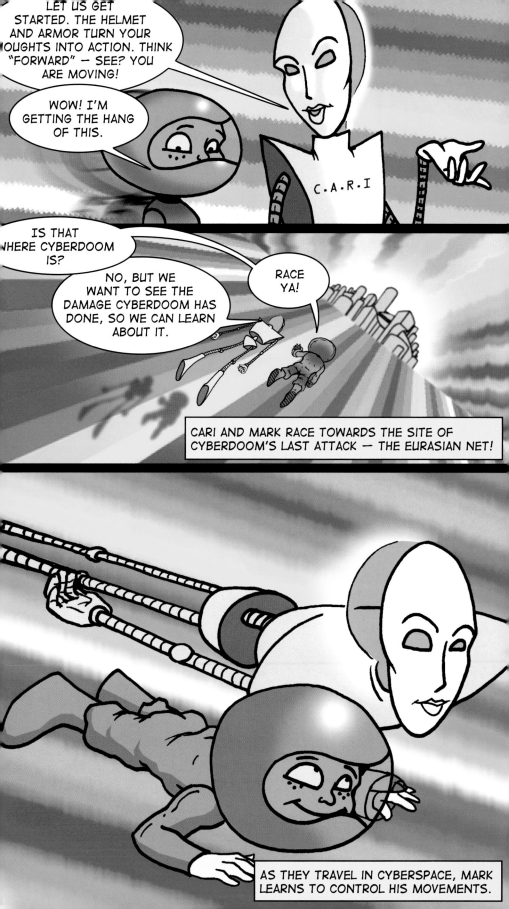

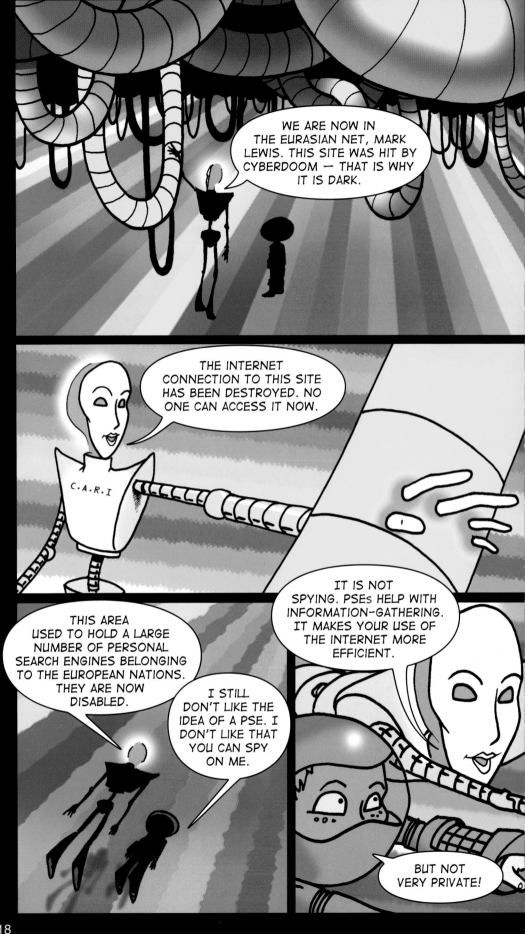

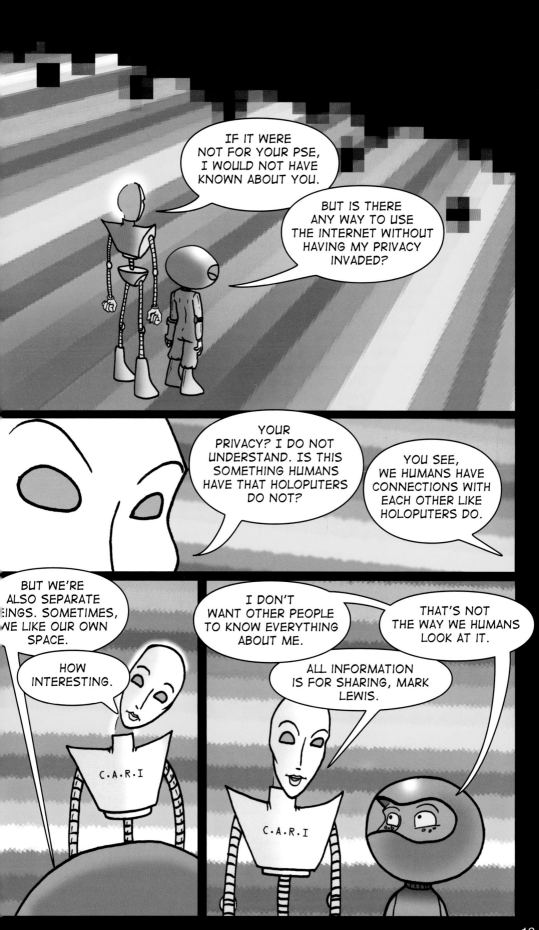

FAMOUS VIRUSES

In medicine, a virus is a kind of germ that spreads disease from person to person. In the computer world, a virus is a program designed to harm computers. Viruses erase or move files on your computer. They can cause your computer to stop working.

1998 The virus "Chernobyl" was discovered. It could use up all the memory on a computer, prevent anti-virus software from running, and even erase a computer's hard drive.

1999 "Melissa" infected more than 100,000 computers over three days. It spread via e-mail.

2000 Like Melissa, the "ILOVEYOU" virus spread via the user's e-mail. It attacked and erased files on a computer's hard drive.

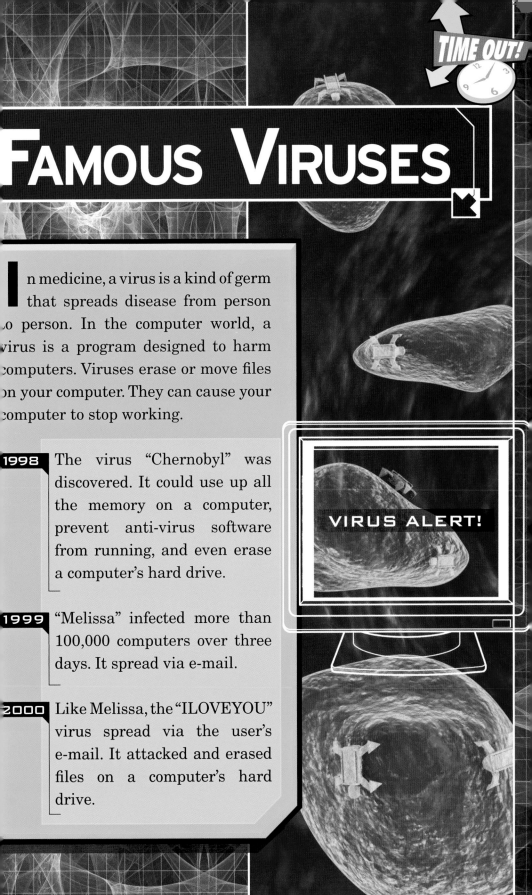

VIRUS ALERT!

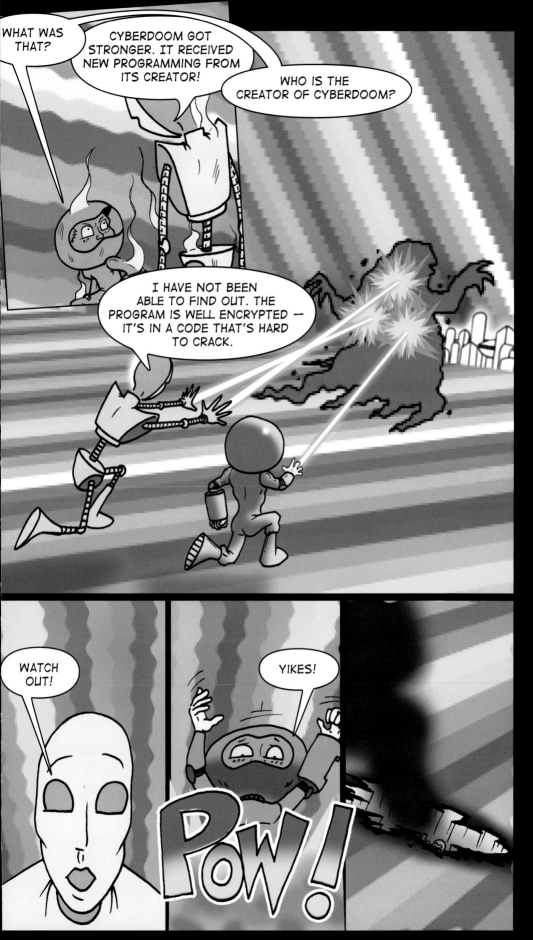

HACKER HALL OF SHAME

Hackers break into personal or business computers to destroy or steal confidential information.

KEVIN POULSEN

In 1990, he took over all the telephone lines of a Los Angeles radio station so that he could win a radio contest for a Porsche. The FBI caught up with him, and in 1994 he was sentenced to 51 months in jail.

VLADIMIR LEVIN

In 1995, he was the mastermind behind a hacker gang that tricked an American bank's computers into spitting out $10 million. He was arrested and spent three years in jail. He was ordered to pay the bank his share from the heist.

MAFIABOY

In 2000, this Canadian teen sent vast amounts of data to the CNN website, causing it to fail. He also hacked other major websites, causing an estimated $1.7 billion in damages. In 2001, he was sentenced to eight months in a detention center.

EASY AS PI

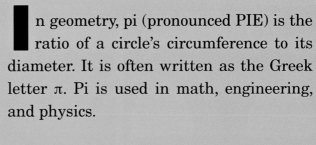

In geometry, pi (pronounced PIE) is the ratio of a circle's circumference to its diameter. It is often written as the Greek letter π. Pi is used in math, engineering, and physics.

Pi is often rounded off to 3.14, but it is actually an infinite decimal, meaning that its decimal places have no end. One supercomputer has calculated pi to over one trillion digits, but no one has been able to find an end or pattern to the number.

Many people make a hobby of memorizing as many decimal places of pi as they can. On July 2, 2005, a Japanese man named Akira Haraguchi broke the world record for the most digits of pi ever recited from memory — 83,431!

Here are the first 100 decimal places of pi: 3.14159265358979323846264338327950288419716939937510582097494459230781640628620899862803482534211706 79.

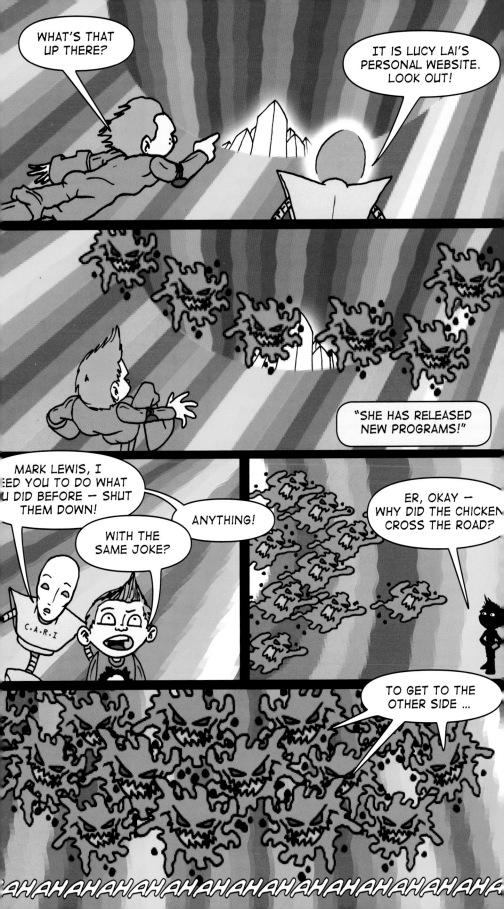

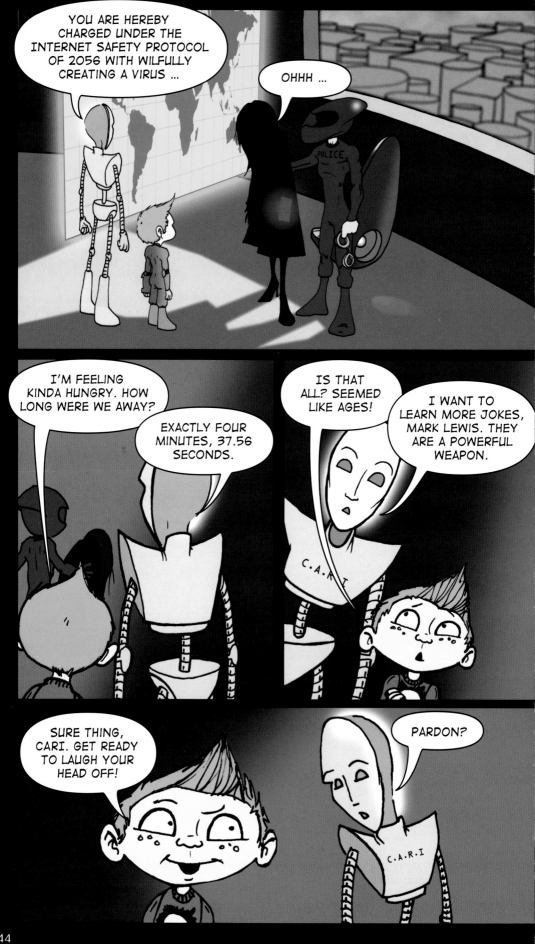

CYBER TALK

Are you familiar with all the words in this list?

ANDROID: a robot that looks human

CYBERSPACE: the world that computer users inhabit when they are online

DISRUPTER: a device that sends out a signal to prevent another signal from working

ENCRYPTED: converted into a secret code to protect information

HOLOGRAM: a three-dimensional image

NANOBOT: a super-tiny robot, about one micrometre (39 microinches) in size

PROTOCOL: a code that allows computers to communicate with one another

VIDSTREAM: a video that you can watch on the Internet

WORM: a type of computer virus that doesn't attach itself to a specific program

What other words can you add to the list to show you are Internet-savvy?

THE FUTURE

Before 1991, only computer scientists and military personnel used the Internet. Today, almost a billion people around the world use the Internet to work, study, and do everything from downloading music to watching baby eagles hatch on the other side of the world!

The new version of the Internet — Internet 2 — allows for greater high-speed transfer of data. Experts think it will change our lives just as much as the first Internet has.